# Where's ITSY BITSY Spider?™

## by
## Chuck Whelon

Planet URF
Entertainment®

# Dedication:

"Where's Itsy Bitsy Spider?" is dedicated to Tina, who makes it all possible.

# Acknowledgements:

This first edition of "Where's Itsy Bitsy Spider?"™ was brought to life by all the kind folks who backed it on Kickstarter. Thanks to you, and to all my friends and family in the UK and USA, and readers across the world, for all your love and support over the years.

Many of the scenes in this book were first published by the UK's Daily Mail newspaper during the summers of 2020 & 2021, as part of their annual treasure hunt. The San Francisco scenes were originally commissioned by Lauren Davis for Skodaman Press. Thanks also to my agent, Beehive Illustration, for giving me the opportunity to develop my art in this space.

# Also Available:

Planet Urf Entertainment
chuck@PlanetUrf.com
www.PlanetUrf.com

"Planet Urf Entertainment"® is a Registered Trademark of Chuck Whelon

ISBN: 978-1-7351717-5-3

# Where's iTsY BiTsY Spider?™

## Chuck Whelon

## Summer Saturday

Tonight, the normally very normal city of Sirenchester in southern England is hosting the world's biggest talent contest: "Everyone's a Bit of a Star!" Itsy Bitsy and friends will be performing their act, and this afternoon they are out exploring the town.

*...but where's Itsy Bitsy Spider?*

I spy 12 birds!

I spy 9 mice!

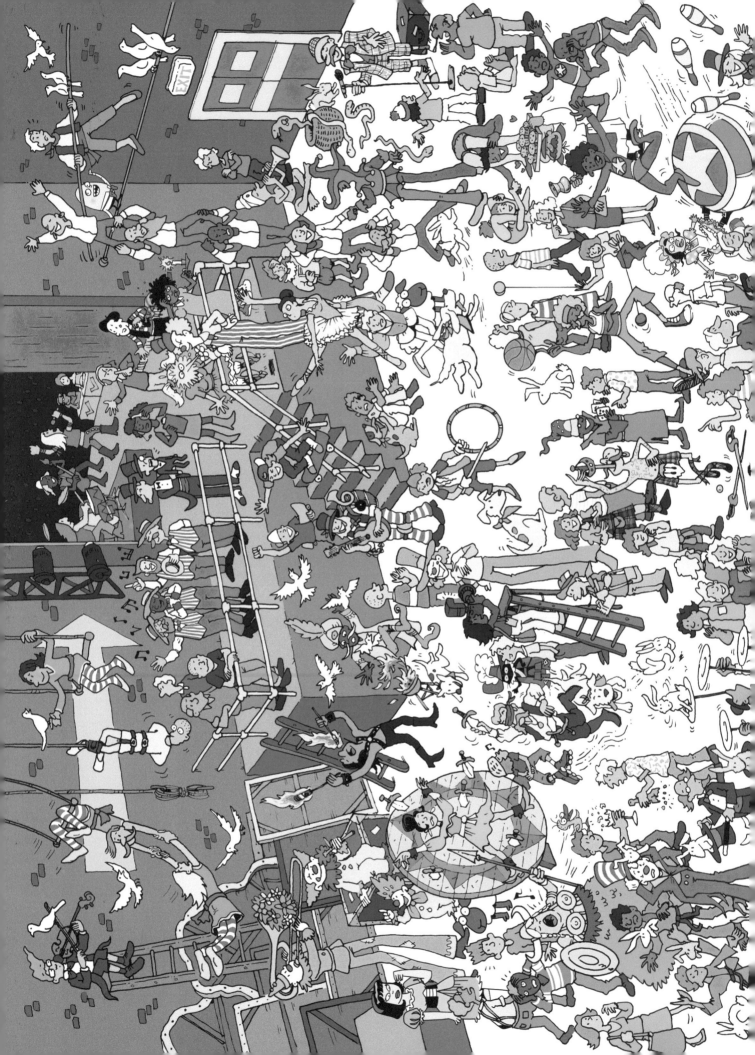

I spy 8 pink rabbits!

I spy 6 dogs!

## The Talent Show

It's exciting to be backstage at the talent contest broadcast. The opening act is on already, and the studio audience is loving it. Itsy Bitsy and friends are up next, so get it together everybody!

...but where's *Itsy Bitsy Spider?*

## Trafalgar Square

Hooray! Yes, you guessed it: Itsy Bitsy and friends have won a trip to London to visit the Queen. There's so much to do in the city. Puss in Boots hopes to check in on his old pal, Dick Whittington's Cat.

*...but where's Itsy Bitsy Spider?*

I spy 15 pigeons!

I spy 7 musical instruments!

## Command Performance

Itsy Bitsy and friends now get to perform in London's West End, with an orchestra and full chorus. At first, the audience is bewildered by the musical show's originality. By the final curtain, it is a smash-hit sensation.

*...but where's Itsy Bitsy Spider?*

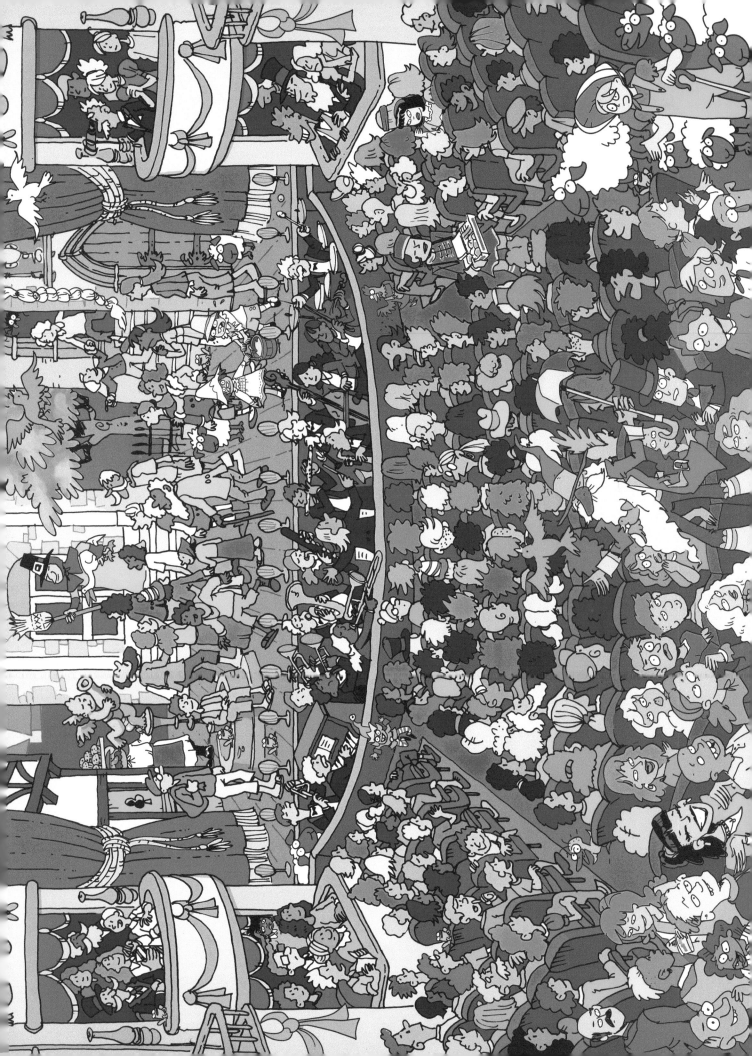

## Grand Slam

Following their success on the London Stage, Itsy Bitsy and friends are now celebrities. Today they are guests at an international tennis tournament. Unfortunately not everyone is paying attention as the winning point is scored.

...but where's Itsy Bitsy Spider?

I spy 10 tennis balls!

I spy 4 Dogs... and lots of hats!

## Beside the Seaside

It's hard work being famous, so Itsy Bitsy and friends take a little beach holiday. Everyone has a great day out, even though things are a bit hectic. Don't forget the sunscreen!

...but where's Itsy Bitsy Spider?

## Here's to History

Humpty Dumpty is a big fan of history, so the friends decide to spend a day at a local History Fair. There sure was a lot of history in the past. Itsy Bitsy is glad to live in the future, where things are much better now.

...but where's Itsy Bitsy Spider?

I spy 3 crowns!

I spy 10 tall top hats!

# Village Cricket

Itsy Bitsy and friends are in the village of Little Picklington for the annual fête and charity cricket match. Ahh... now this is very relaxing. What a perfect way to spend a lazy August afternoon.

*...but where's Itsy Bitsy Spider?*

I spy 5 ducks!

I spy 6 cricket bats!

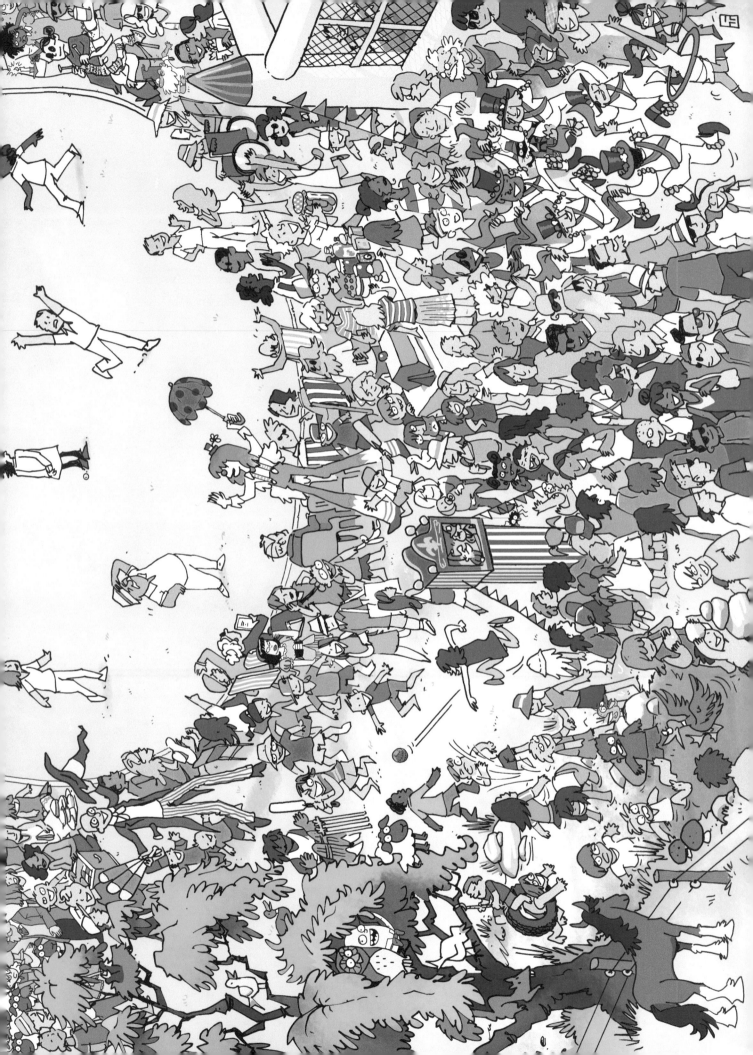

## Culture Vultures

Itsy Bitsy and friends have been booked to perform at a classical music festival. Their act transcends genres and brings great joy to all who witness it. As headliners, they will not appear until later in the evening, so for now they get to have fun.

*...but where's Itsy Bitsy Spider?*

## Flying Down to Rio

Next stop on their world tour, is Rio de Janeiro. Itsy Bitsy and friends are being represented as floats in the annual carnival parade. It's another marvelous night of fun. Fame is fleeting, so everyone enjoys it while they can.

*...but where's Itsy Bitsy Spider?*

I spy 6 red noses!

I spy 8 green wigs!

## Muni Meltdown

Itsy Bitsy and friends visit San Francisco, California. There is a bit of a kerfuffle when their bus gets delayed. It looks like everyone is going to have to get out and find alternative means of transportation.

...but where's Itsy Bitsy Spider?

I spy 5 bicycles!

I spy 6 smartphones!

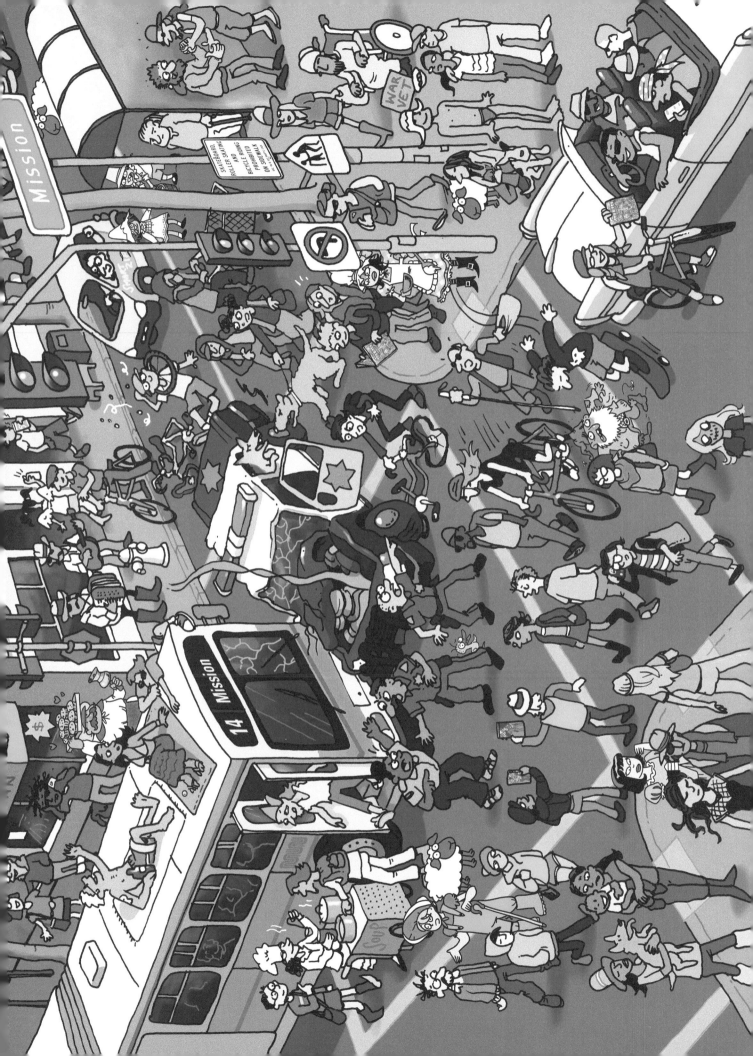

# Sci-Fi San Francisco

It's time to go home, but first Itsy Bitsy and friends are scheduled to appear at a fan convention. They meet many new friends of all shapes and sizes. Or was it all just a dream? It does get very exhausting jetting round the world on the red-eye.

*...but where's Itsy Bitsy Spider?*

I spy 7 robots!

I spy 5 apes!

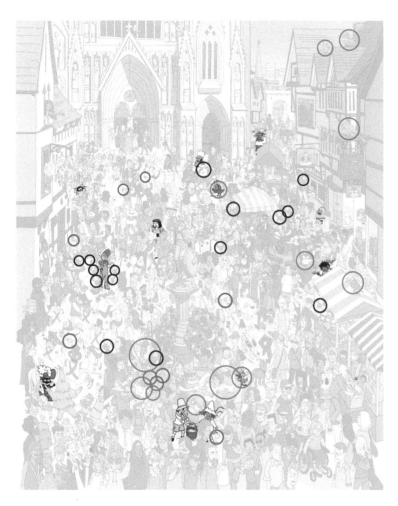

## 01: Summer Saturday

**9 Mice**
12 Birds
**15 Sheep**

### Bonus Points:
- ☐ 5 dogs
- ☐ A crying mother
- ☐ A crying child
- ☐ A baby green tentacle monster
- ☐ 2 Waving gargoyles

## 02: The Talent Show

**8 Pink Rabbits**
6 Dogs
**9 Sheep**

### Bonus Points:
- ☐ 15 White rabbits
- ☐ 2 Mime artists
- ☐ 14 White doves
- ☐ 3 Guitars
- ☐ 5 Balls

## 03: Trafalgar Square

15 Pigeons
7 Musical Instruments
**14 Sheep**

### Bonus Points:
- ■ A man with a tiger
- ■ A laughing policeman
- ■ A living statue
- ■ 6 Soccer balls
- ■ An engagement ring

## 04: Command Performance

8 Bluebirds
1 Dancing Elf    9 Frogs
**9 Sheep**

### Bonus Points:
- ■ A woman eating popcorn
- ■ A man with 3-D glasses
- ■ A blue hat
- ■ A cherub
- ■ 12 Mustaches

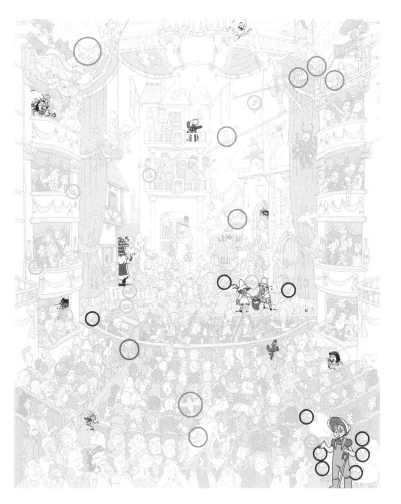

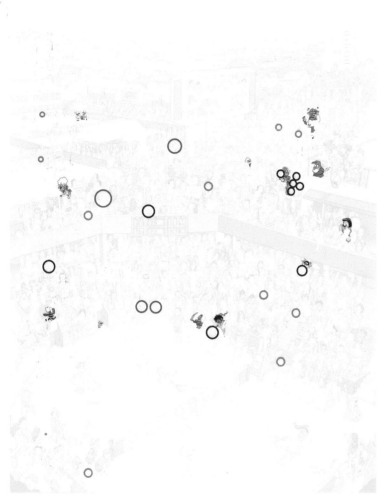

## 05: Grand Slam

10 Tennis Balls
4 Dogs
**9 Sheep**

GUFFY

### Bonus Points:
- 2 rabbits
- A robot
- A gargoyle party
- Sherlock Holmes & Dr. Watson
- A bow tie

Who will reap the wheat?

How did you get that thing past security?

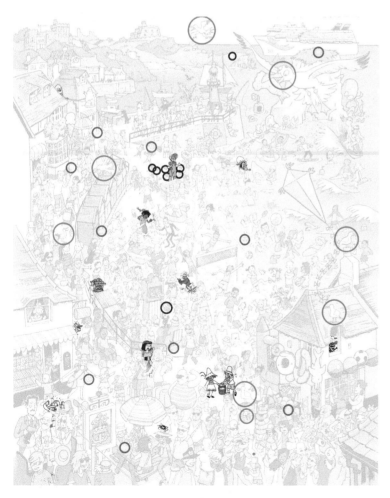

## 06: Beside the Seaside

8 Seagulls
10 Eggs
**8 Sheep**

STRESSY

### Bonus Points:
- A calico cat
- A seal
- A mermaid
- A rubber ducky
- A traffic jam

Who will thresh the wheat?

I think that might be sand.

## 07: Here's to History

3 Crowns
10 Tall Top Hats
**6 Sheep**

LUMP

**Bonus Points:**
- ■ A centurion in a Centurion
- ■ Charles I vs. Ollie Cromwell
- ■ A quill pen
- ■ Johnny Appleseed
- ■ A London bus

Who will sift the wheat?

Things sure were harder in the past.

5 Ducks
6 Cricket Bats
**6 Sheep**

TWITCHY

Who will carry the wheat to the mill?

The supermarket's closer.

## 09: Culture Vultures

3 Dogs
8 Rabbits
**11 Sheep**

### Bonus Points:
- ☐ A small horse
- ☐ A strawberry cake
- ☐ 11 Birds
- ☐ An ear trumpet
- ☐ An egg

## 10: Flying Down to Rio

6 Red Noses
8 Green Wigs
**6 Sheep**

### Bonus Points:
- ☐ 3 Blue and yellow hats
- ☐ A woman in a toga
- ☐ A man blowing a trumpet
- ☐ A froggy umbrella
- ☐ A photographer

5 Bicycles
6 Smartphones
**4 Sheep**

## 12: Sci-Fi San Francisco

7 Robots
5 Apes
**3 Sheep**

### Bonus Points:
- [ ] 13 Cars and trucks
- [ ] 2 Green girls
- [ ] A grown green tentacle monster
- [ ] 4 Top Hats
- [ ] 12 Animals of the Chinese zodiac

CPSIA information can be obtained
at www.ICGtesting.com
Printed in the USA
BVHW022013070622
638335BV00020B/54